Josie the Mermaid

Written and Illustrated by Thomas Seator

Fulton Books
Meadville, PA

Published by Fulton Books 2022

The Bill of Rights makes no mention of the pursuit of happiness, however due to a Supreme Court ruling Meyer vs Nebraska 1923, it was decided that the pursuit of happiness can be considered as part of the umbrella policy of the fourteenth amendment.

ISBN 979-8-88505-682-3 (hardcover)
ISBN 979-8-88505-681-6 (digital)

Printed in the United States of America

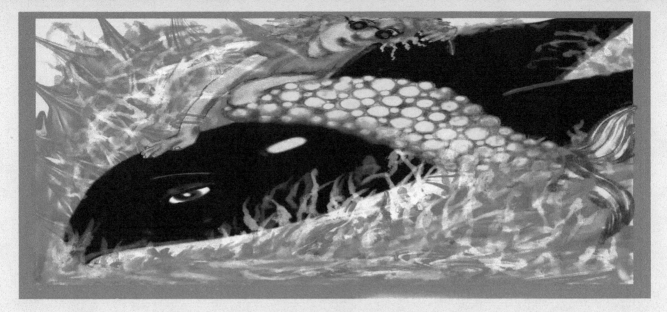

This book is dedicated to Pat Patrick, a retired schoolteacher, who has spent her entire life encouraging the love of reading and learning. Also, her granddaughter, Josie, is the inspiration for this book. I wish everyone to dream big and live their dream. Your imagination can take you on the most amazing adventures.

Book Reports Tomorrow !

Everything was gray. It was a world with out happiness.

1

Book reports due Friday

Subject: The Bill of Rights

Choose one of The Bill Of Rights

from the bowl on my desk.

No one liked our substitute teacher, Mrs. Cranky!

"I got freedom of assembly. What did you get, Josie?" "The pursuit of happiness," Josie grumbled.

3

While walking home from school,
she stumbled acrossed a ladybug
in need of help.

4

So, Josie untangled the ladybug
from the grass and freed her.

She had no idea this small act of kindness would change her world forever.

Hundreds of ladybugs instantaneously appeared and showered her with kisses. "Thank you for saving our friend," they all chanted in melodic harmony.

Ladybug kisses have the power to transform you into anything you wish. On that day, Josie chose to be a mermaid. 8

All the colors in this new world
were so beautiful.

Making new friends was so easy.

The whale rides were awesome!

I even got to encounter two lovely
whale sharks.

Playing tennis with a pink
flamingo was enjoyable and challenging.

13

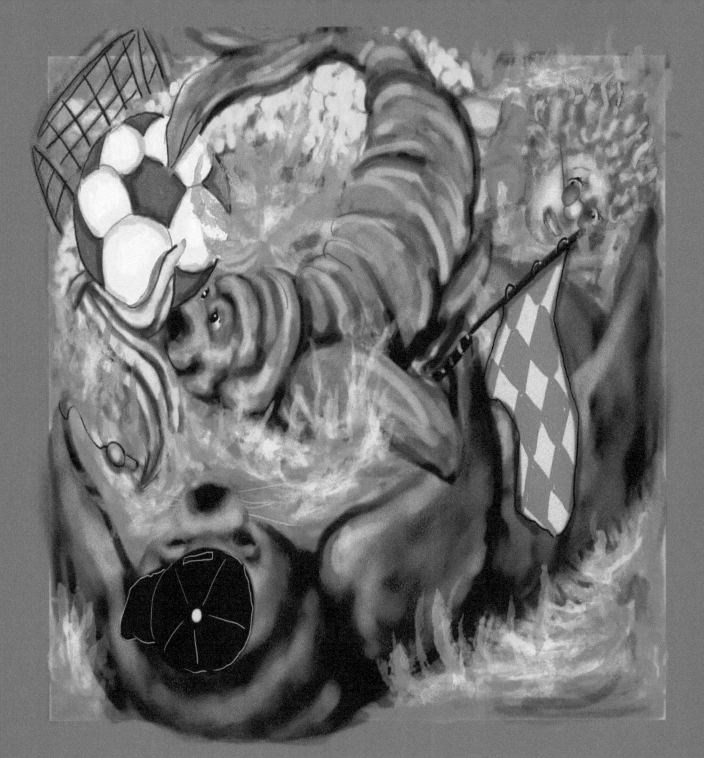

The seals were victorious in our soccer match.

While I was learning the Turtle dance,
it started to rain.

I got invited for tea and cakes with an octopus. 16

I was having such a good time playing with my new friends.

I wanted this day to last forever.

Josie`s parents and her dog,Henrick,
went looking for her every where.
They started to get very worried !

"Hello everyone, we are looking for our daughter, Josie. Have you seen her?" Josie`s mother spoke in a distressed tone.

"Your parents are looking for you.
It`s time for you to go home." Wylie
the walrus whispered.

"What are you doing out there.
It`s a school night!" Josie`s dad
yelled in a petulant tone!

So, she got out of the water and
walked home with her mom and dad.

The next day as Josie talked about her day pursuing happiness, the classroom started to eradicate the gloomy, gray, morose saturation of repetitive humdrum

23

After her presentation, exuberant joy filled the classroom. All the gray frowzy film of hopelees despair evaporated, and the atmosphere of infinite creative abundance permeated every crevasse of the chamber.

"You can be a mermaid on weekends and non school nights." Josie`s parents pledged to the new creative imagination bill of rights pursuit of happiness treaty.

"Next weeks topic, constitutional law." Mrs. Cranky snarled!
The end?

Yummy
Tummy
RECIPES

Artful
Snacks

by Marilyn LaPenta

Consultant:
Sharon Richter, MS, RD, CDN

BEARPORT
PUBLISHING

NEW YORK, NEW YORK

Credits

All food illustrations by Kim Jones

Publisher: Kenn Goin
Senior Editor: Lisa Wiseman
Creative Director: Spencer Brinker
Design: Debrah Kaiser

Library of Congress Cataloging-in-Publication Data

LaPenta, Marilyn.
  Artful snacks / by Marilyn LaPenta ; consultant, Sharon Richter.
    p. cm. — (Yummy tummy recipes)
  Includes bibliographical references and index.
  ISBN-13: 978-1-61772-307-0 (library binding)
  ISBN-10: 1-61772-307-X (library binding)
  1. Snack foods—Juvenile literature. 2. Cookbooks—Juvenile literature. 3. Cooking—Juvenile literature. I. Title.
  TX740.L26 2012
  641.5'3—dc23
                          2011019695

For more information, write to Bearport Publishing Company, Inc., 45 West 21st Street, Suite 3B, New York, New York 10010. Printed in the United States of America in North Mankato, Minnesota.

073011
042711CGE

10 9 8 7 6 5 4 3 2 1

Contents

Making Artful Snacks 4

Getting Started 6

Cheese and Fruit Kebabs 8

Quick Peanut Butter Bars 9

Nutty Snack Mix 10

Healthy Lemon Hummus 11

Frozen Fruit Pops 12

Cheese Tortilla with Salsa 13

Party Pretzels 14

Bug Parade 15

Chocolate-Dipped Fruit 16

Apple Puzzle 17

Great Guacamole Dip 18

Deviled Egg Delights 19

Pizza Bites 20

Yogurt, Granola, and Fruit Creations 21

Healthy Tips 22

Glossary 23

Index 24

Bibliography 24

Read More 24

Learn More Online 24

About the Author 24

Making Artful Snacks

Get ready to make some of the yummiest snacks you'll ever put in your tummy! The delicious recipes in *Artful Snacks* are super easy to make. Many of them come with ideas for creating treats that are visually interesting as well as tasty. Once you make a recipe, try your own ideas for making the snack look like a work of art!

The great thing about making your own food is that you know exactly what goes into it. When you make your own snacks, for example, you can carefully choose healthy ingredients. You can limit items with **preservatives**, which are not always good for your body. You can also choose **low-fat** dairy products instead of full-fat items to make your snacks more heart healthy. Too many calories, especially from foods high in fat or sugar, may lead to **obesity**. Use the ideas on page 22 for making the healthy snacks in this cookbook even more nutritious.

Getting Started

Use these cooking and safety tips, as well as the tool guide, to make the best snacks you've ever tasted.

Tips

Here are a few tips to get your cooking off to a great start.

- Quickly check out the Prep Time, Tools, and Servings information at the top of each recipe. It will tell you how long the recipe takes to prepare, the tools you'll need, and the number of people the recipe serves.

- Once you pick a recipe, set out the tools and ingredients that you will need on your worktable.

- Before and after cooking, wash your hands well with warm soapy water.

- Wash fruits and vegetables with edible skins before using them in the recipes.

- Put on an apron or a smock to protect your clothes.

- Roll up long shirtsleeves to keep them clean.

- Tie back or cover long hair to keep it out of the food.

- *Very important*: Keep the adults happy by cleaning up the kitchen when you've finished cooking.

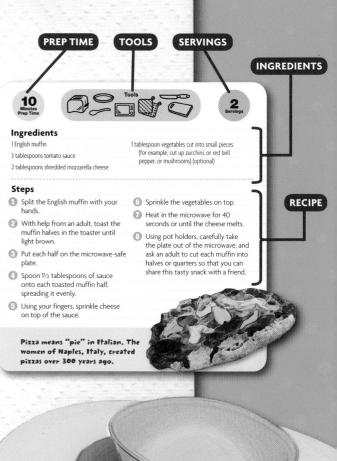

PREP TIME   **TOOLS**   **SERVINGS**   **INGREDIENTS**

10 Minutes Prep Time   Tools   **2** Servings

Ingredients

1 English muffin

3 tablespoons tomato sauce

2 tablespoons shredded mozzarella cheese

1 tablespoon vegetables cut into small pieces (for example, cut up zucchini, or red bell pepper, or mushrooms) (optional)

Steps   **RECIPE**

1. Split the English muffin with your hands.
2. With help from an adult, toast the muffin halves in the toaster until light brown.
3. Put each half on the microwave-safe plate.
4. Spoon 1½ tablespoons of sauce onto each toasted muffin half, spreading it evenly.
5. Using your fingers, sprinkle cheese on top of the sauce.
6. Sprinkle the vegetables on top.
7. Heat in the microwave for 40 seconds or until the cheese melts.
8. Using pot holders, carefully take the plate out of the microwave, and ask an adult to cut each muffin into halves or quarters so that you can share this tasty snack with a friend.

Pizza means "pie" in Italian. The women of Naples, Italy, created pizzas over 300 years ago.

Be Safe

Cook safely by having an adult around to help with these activities:

- Using a sharp knife or peeler
- Using the stove, microwave, blender, food processor, toaster, or other electrical appliances
- Removing hot pans from the oven (Always use pot holders.)
- Frying foods on top of the stove (Keep the heat as low as possible to avoid burns from oil splatter.)

Tools You Need

Many of the recipes in this book require a stove, refrigerator, toaster, or microwave oven. Most recipes also require four or five other common kitchen tools.*

Sharp knife

Butter knife

Paring knife

Mixing spoon

Spoon

Wooden spoon

Serving spoon

Fork

Ice cream scoop

Scissors

Spatula

Masher

Small cookie cutters

Apple corer

Can opener

Cutting board

Colander

Measuring spoons

Measuring cups

Small bowl

Medium mixing bowl

Baking sheet

Small plate

Small serving dish

Serving bowl and tray

Microwave-safe plate

Medium frying pan

9" X 9" baking pan

Pot

Double boiler (or 2 pots, one that fits inside the other)

Stove

Microwave

Toaster

Pot holders

Long toothpicks

3-ounce paper cups

Plastic wrap

1-gallon plastic sealable bag

Aluminum foil

Wax paper

Blender

Tall glass

*If you do not have a particular tool, you can usually substitute another. For example, if you do not have a particular kind of knife or spoon—another kind will often work just fine.

Cheese and Fruit Kebabs

10 Minutes Prep Time

Tools

4 Servings

Ingredients

¼ pound cheese (cheddar, Monterey Jack, American, or any combination of the three)

1 cup assorted fresh fruit pieces (Choose your favorites!)

Steps

1. Ask an adult to use the knife to cut the cheese into 1- to 2-inch cubes on the cutting board. Or if you have small cookie cutters, press them into the cheese to make different shapes.

2. Take a long toothpick and slide the fruit and cheese onto it—one piece of cheese, followed by a piece of fruit, followed by a piece of cheese, and so on—to create a kebab.

3. Repeat Step 2 until 4 toothpicks are filled. Then enjoy your colorful work of art.

Health Tip

All types of fruits are high in vitamins and **minerals**.

Archaeologists have found the remains of what they think was cheese in Egyptian tombs that are more than 4,000 years old.

Quick Peanut Butter Bars

5 Minutes Prep Time*

*Plus 1 hour to cool

Tools

15 Servings

Health Tip

If you are allergic to peanut butter, ask a parent if you can try a different kind of nut butter, such as almond or cashew.

Ingredients

1 cup peanut butter

¾ cup honey

2 cups uncooked rolled oats

½ cup dried cranberries (or any dried fruit of your choice)

½ cup sunflower seeds (or other seeds or nuts of your choice)

Steps

1. Put the peanut butter and honey in the frying pan. With help from an adult, warm the ingredients over low heat on the stove top. Stir with the spoon until the ingredients are mixed and runny.

2. Stir in the oats, dried cranberries, and sunflower seeds until everything is nicely blended together.

3. Carefully pour the mixture into a 9" x 9" pan, using a spoon to help. Then, use the spatula to press it evenly into the pan.

4. Let the mixture cool for 1 hour and then ask an adult to cut it into 15 bars of equal size.

5. The bars do not need to be refrigerated. Just wrap them in aluminum foil. Grab one whenever you need a quick snack!

Americans eat about 500 million pounds of peanut butter every year—enough to cover the floor of the Grand Canyon!

9